# Everybody Jump!

HarperCollins*Children's Books*

First published in India in 2022 by **HarperCollins Children's Books**
An imprint of HarperCollins *Publishers*
Building No 10, Tower A, 4th Floor,
DLF Cyber City, Phase II, Gurugram 122002
www.harpercollins.co.in

2 4 6 8 10 9 7 5 3 1


P-ISBN: 9789356293786
E-ISBN: 9789356293793



Typeset in CookieRunOTF 14 pt/24 by **Shamika Chaves**

Printed and bound by Nutech Print Services - India

HarperCollinsIn

## Ricky

MUHAHAHA! You may know Pang as the group leader, but the true leader is me! You'll understand if you stick around! HAHAHA!

## Oliver

What great weather we have today.
On a day like this, I just want to sit by the lake, eat cookies, and listen to some music.
So... Please don't take my cookies!

## Shasha

I can make anything I put my mind to! So tell me what you need.
But don't go asking for too much, okay?

## PANG

I like anything fun! Join me if you are feeling down.
PANG! A game of cricket will help you feel better!

## Cash

Let's go play right now!!
It'll be fun! Quickly!
Cash has lots of great ideas!

Shasha brought a jump rope
to the cricket field.
She showed her friends
how to jump rope.

WOW!

everyone shouted.
They all wanted to try
jumping rope as well.

Pang was the first one to try.

Cash was next but
he did not want to wait.

"**Cash wants to try!**" Cash cried.
Soon he was on the ground, whining for his turn.

Pang gave the jump rope to Cash.
Just then Ricky also started
whining for his turn.

**"Ricky wants to try too!"** he cried.
Pang, Ricky, and Oliver tried their best, but it wasn't easy.

Waahaa!

Shasha had had enough.

**"You guys can't just whine for what you want!"**

she said.

Her friends weren't very good at taking turns.

Shasha had a great idea.

**"Let's go to my house!**

**I have a lot of jump ropes you can choose from,"** she said.

Shasha had a box full of all types of jump ropes.
Everyone jumped in to find the perfect one for themselves.

The jump rope that
Oliver chose was too small.

**"That's too short for you,**
**silly Oliver."**
Ricky teased.

Ricky also picked a jump rope out of the box,
but Ricky's jump rope was too long.

Ricky tried his best to jump the rope,
but it was not easy.

"That jump rope isn't made for one person,"
Shasha laughed.

Shasha asked Pang and Cash to hold each
end of the jump rope and spin it.
Then Shasha jumped in.

"**Ricky! Oliver! Jump in!**" Shasha shouted.
Ricky jumped in, but Oliver was too tall.

Everyone was having fun jumping rope together.
Oliver was spinning the rope for
his friends because he was too tall.

But he also wanted to
try jumping.

Oliver was not having fun anymore.

**"I'm the only one that turns the rope!**

**I want to try jumping as well!"** Oliver shouted.

Upset that he could not jump with his friends,
Oliver hid in the woods.

Pang and his friends came up with a plan to help Oliver join in the fun as well.

Pang and Ricky stood on large steps to become much taller.

With the steps, Oliver could finally jump with his friends.

In the end, everyone could have fun.

The **Cricket Pang** series is a set of picture books with charming stories based on lovable animal characters. The overall theme of the books is cricket, which besides being a very popular sport for children, also lends a unique flavour to this series. Children will love the main character, Pang, and his bunch of friends. Each book highlights important values through engaging stories and endearing characters. With their simple vocabulary and sentence structure, these books are perfect for early readers.

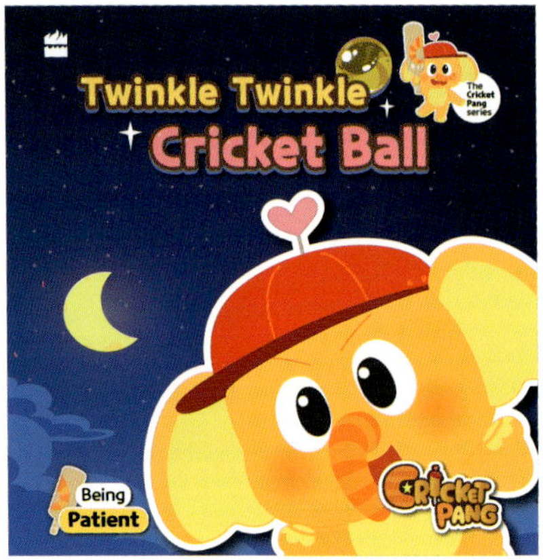


**Being patient!**

**Being fair!**

**Being kind!**

**Being smart!**